BIBLICAL FOUNDATIONS

FOUNDATIONAL BIBLE STUDIES FOR BUILDING STRONG DISCIPLES

D1509814

BIBLICAL FOUNDATIONS

Copyright © 1998 by Rice Broocks, Phil Bonasso and Steve Murrell
Published by Every Nation Productions
P.O. Box 1787, Brentwood, TN 37024
www.everynationstore.com • E-Mail: orders@everynation.org

Printed in the Republic of the Philippines.
April 1998
January 1999
April 1999
October 1999
July 2000

Printed in Nashville, TN.
November 2001
February 2003
October 2003
June 2004

Introduction

The most important thing for a person who wants to become a champion for Christ is to build a strong foundation. This is especially critical in light of the ever-changing uncertainties of modern life. It is an understatement to say that the culture around us has become openly hostile to the Christian faith. Society says, "Sure, you can be a Christian, as long as you keep your beliefs to yourself. But if you start preaching in public, get ready for a fight."

You must have the kind of foundation that can withstand a spiritual hurricane of opposition. Jesus said, "Everyone who comes to Me, and hears My words, and acts upon them is like a man building a house, who dug deep and laid a foundation upon the rock" (Luke 6:47-48). Christ pointed out that house stands when the storms come. But, He added, the foolish man who hears His words and fails to act upon them is like the man who builds his house without a foundation. The storm wipes him out. The large number of spiritual calamities for such a man reveals his inadequate foundation.

However, laying a foundation is not that exciting. Who wants to work so hard on something that will never be seen? Well, once your building is complete it will make a great difference. Bad foundations show up through cracks in the walls and ceilings. The cracks warn that something isn't right. Shortcuts at the bottom make for disasters on top.

I once took a team of students to the island of Guam for an evangelistic outreach. I should have known that something was amiss when they handed me my room key at the hotel: "Sir, your room number is 911." Everyone joked how we would be getting all the emergency calls. Little did we realize that we soon would be the ones in trouble.

Two days later, one of the century's worst earthquakes - 8.2 on the Richter scale   hit the island. Even more incredible, it lasted for sixty quivering, gut-wrenching, fear-riveting seconds. As we sat in room 911, it seemed to explode. The television set hurtled to the floor. Slammed from its perch, the sliding glass door shattered into a million slivers. We ran for the fire escape, but that route was blocked.

Not knowing where else to go, we stood on the balcony to ride out the most terrifying minute of our lives. As each second ticked by, we felt certain that the building would collapse. Just as it felt like the hotel would rip in half, all motion ceased. We ran down the steps into the street and began singing the praises of God. I never had an easier time telling strangers about the Lord!

The next day we toured the island to assess the damage. What stuck out was a new hotel on the verge of collapse. Two floors had disintegrated and the rest of the structure tilted like the Leaning Tower of Pisa. It looked solid before the quake, but the shaking revealed the faulty workmanship. The hotel had to be torn down. I couldn't help comparing that razed structure to our accommodations. As much as I give God the glory for saving our lives, I also thank the engineers who built the hotel, particularly the ones who laid the foundation. They appreciated the instability of an earthquake zone, so they built the foundation strong enough, yet with enough flexibility, to take the worst shaking. Apparently the builders of the other hotel took shortcuts.

How irresponsible it is not to take account of the "fault line" we are living on in this generation. Sin has warped the entire cosmos. Everywhere we see massive upheaval. We cannot simply lay any foundation: "For no one can lay a foundation other than the one already laid, which is Jesus Christ" (1 Cor. 3:11). We must dig down deep and tear out everything that is hostile to Christ.

Whenever a professing Christian fails in a public way, we stand before the ruins asking, "Why?" Later, after a spiritual autopsy, we discover there was never a solid foundation in the person's life. Sure, they believed in Jesus, but they had no real understanding of repentance or His lordship. Many of these casualties were never taught the need to open their lives to fellow believers who could challenge them and stand with them during times of temptation. Who knows what disasters could have been prevented if there had been "building inspectors" examining the foundations.

Biblical Foundations will give you a look at the glorious difference a strong foundation makes. II Timothy 3:16 says the word of God is profitable "for teaching, for reproof, for correction, for training in righteousness." We all like the teaching part, but we are not too thrilled about the reproof and correction part.

But the latter is where the men are separated from the boys. Better yet, where the winners are separated from the losers. Who is willing to let the Lord reprove and correct him through other men? This shouldn't be so difficult. Individuals who want to be great athletes, pianists, gymnasts, scientists, you name it, learn from others teaching and correcting them. So it must be with the sons of Light.

Most would say we are living in the greatest time in human history. Technology has drawn the world so tightly together that we can realistically hope to preach to everyone who is open to the gospel. Yet, with all the opportunity that is before us, the challenge remains for us not to present a Christianity that is weak and anemic.

The early church turned their world upside down, with no TV, Internet, or supersonic jets, not even a sound system. What spoke to pagans was the reality that Christ had made new men and women out of those who truly followed Him. The disciples were able to withstand the pressure of the entire Roman Empire that came crashing down on them. They were ready to lay down their lives for the cause of Jesus Christ. Let us pray that a new generation of such warriors rises up and pledges their all, so that our world will turn back to righteousness.

Rice Broocks
President, Morning Star International

Contents

Sin
&
Salvation

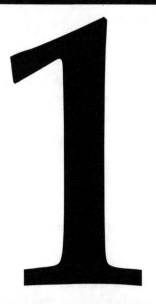

*What must I do
to be saved?*
Acts 2:37

LESSON 1 The Original Sin

Before we can understand salvation and appreciate the fact that Jesus is our Savior, we must first understand why man needs a savior and what he needs to be saved from. In short, we must understand the seriousness of sin and its eternal consequences.

1. What was God's command? Genesis 2:16,17

_____

_____

Read Genesis 3:1-13.

2. How did Adam and Eve respond to God's command?

_____

_____

3. Who tempted Eve?

_____

4. Adam and Eve ate the forbidden fruit. They disobeyed God. They sinned. How did they react after their *eyes were opened and they realized they were naked?*

v. 7 _____

v. 8 _____

v. 10 _____

5. How did God respond to Adam and Eve's sin?

v. 8,9 _____

Notice the different responses to man's sin:
- Man covered up and hid from God.
- God sought man.

Things have not changed much since the beginning. After thousands of years and countless sins, man still hides and God still seeks. This is the starting point of understanding salvation.

Personal Application
What did you learn from this lesson and how will you apply it to your life?

_____

_____

_____

The Origin of Sin

The Bible teaches us that sin entered the world as a result of the transgression of Adam and Eve in paradise. The first sin was occasioned by the temptation of Satan in the form of a serpent, who sowed in man's heart the seeds of distrust and unbelief. Scripture clearly indicates that the serpent, who appears as the tempter in the story of the fall, was an instrument of Satan. The first sin consisted in man's eating of the tree of the knowledge of good and evil. This eating was sinful simply because God had forbidden it. It clearly showed that man was not willing to subject his will unconditionally to the will of God, and comprised several elements. In the intellect it revealed itself as unbelief and pride; in the will as the desire to be like God; and in the affections as unholy satisfaction in eating of the forbidden fruit. As a result of it, man lost the image of God in the restricted sense, became guilty and utterly corrupt, and fell under the sway of death. (Berkhof, Summary of Christian Doctrine, page 74)

LESSON 2   The Results of Sin

1. What does iniquity do to man's relationship with God? Isaiah 59:1,2

_____

_____

2. Describe sinful man's condition: Romans 3:9-20,23

v. 9 _____

v. 10 _____

v. 11 _____

v. 11 _____

v. 12 _____

v. 12 _____

v. 12 _____

v. 13,14 _____

v. 16 _____

v. 17 _____

v. 18 _____

v. 23 _____

3. What are the wages of sin? Romans 6:23

_____

_____

4. What follows immediately after death? Hebrews 9:27

_____

5. How does the Bible describe eternal judgment?

Matthew 25:41 _____

Revelation 20:11-15 _____

Revelation 21:8 _____

All sin is rebellion against the holy nature of God. Because of sin, man is separated from God and doomed to an eternity away from his presence.

Personal Application
What did you learn from this lesson and how will you apply it to your life?

_____

_____

_____

LESSON 3   God's Solution for Sin

1. What does Paul call eternal life? Romans 6:23

_____

2. Why did Jesus come into the world? John 3:16;17

_____

3. What is necessary for the forgiveness of sins? Hebrews 9:22

_____

4. What does the blood of Jesus do for us?

Romans 5:9 _____

_____

Ephesians 1:7 _____

_____

Ephesians 2:13 _____

_____

1 John 1:7 _____

_____

Revelation 1:5 _____

_____

5. What did Jesus do for us on the cross?

1 Peter 2:24 _____

_____

2 Corinthians 5:21 _____

_____

Galatians 3:13,14 _____

_____

6. What was God's solution for man's sin? Isaiah 53:6

_____

7. What happens when we receive Jesus as Lord and Savior?
John 1:12,13

_____

_____

8. What did Jesus say must happen before we see and enter the Kingdom of God? John 3:3-7

_____

_____

9. What do the following verses teach about being born of God?

John 1:13 _____

_____

1 Peter 1:23 _____

_____

1 John 3:9 _____

_____

1 John 4:7 _____

_____

1 John 5:4 _____

_____

10. What does Paul say about those who are in Christ?
2 Corinthians 5:17

_____

_____

Because God is holy and just, he cannot let sin go unpunished. Because he is love, he desires to redeem his creation. In order to be just and justifier, God sent his son to earth to pay the penalty for man's sin.

Personal Application

What did you learn from this lesson and how will you apply it to your life?

_____

_____

_____

Have you come to the place in your spiritual life where you know for sure that if you were to die today you would spend eternity in Heaven?
   o Yes   o No   o Not Sure

Suppose you died and God asked, "Why should I let you into my Heaven?" what would you say?

_____

_____

_____

_____

LESSON 4 By Grace Through Faith

1. Is it possible to be saved by our own good works?   How are we saved?
Ephesians 2:8,9

_____

2. Is it possible to be saved by keeping the law? What does the law do? Romans 3:20

_____

3. What does God's grace teach the believer? Titus 2:11,12

_____

_____

4. Why did God save us? Titus 3:4,5

_____

5. What did Paul tell the Romans they must do to be saved?
Romans 10:9,10

_____

6. What should all who confess Jesus as Lord do?

    Luke 6:46 _____

    2 Timothy 2:19 _____

7. What is the significance of the resurrection? What if there is no
resurrection? 1 Corinthians 15:14-19

    v. 14 _____

    v. 15 _____

    v. 16 _____

    v. 17 _____

    v. 18 _____

    v. 19 _____

We are dead in sin. We cannot save ourselves. Regardless of who we are,
we need a Savior. Jesus Christ is the only true Savior. By receiving Jesus
as Lord and Savior, we can be saved from sin and its consequences. Our
salvation is based on what Jesus did for us, not what we do for him. It is
by grace through faith.

In order to receive salvation, we must:
    Realize that we are sinners without excuse (Romans 1:20). Only
    through the cross of Christ can we be saved. This should be our
    conclusion after chapter one.

    Recognize that Jesus Christ is the only Savior and Lord. This will
    be covered in another lesson.

    Respond as the original disciples did, by turning from sin and putting
    faith in Christ alone for salvation. This will be covered fully in
    another lesson.

Personal Application
What did you learn from this lesson and how will you apply it to your life?

_____

_____

_____

Write your personal testimony using the following outline.

Before you met Christ. (The Problem)

_____

_____

_____

_____

_____

_____

_____

How you met Christ. (The Solution)

_____

_____

_____

_____

_____

_____

Since you met Christ. (The Change)

_____

_____

_____

_____

_____

_____

Lordship & Obedience

Why do you call me, 'Lord, Lord,'
and do not do what I say?

Luke 6:46

Jesus Is Lord

Jesus is both Lord and Savior. Most people want to be saved from judgment and hell. However, salvation is not available apart from his Lordship. What does Lordship mean? It does not mean salvation depends on our being perfect. Rather, Lordship is the attitude of complete surrender and obedience to Jesus Christ.

1. What did Peter proclaim about Jesus? Acts 2:36

_____

_____

2. What did Paul write about him? Philippians 2:6-11

v. 6 _____

_____

v. 7 _____

_____

v. 8 _____

_____

v. 9 _____

_____

v. 10 _____

_____

v. 11 _____

_____

3. How should we receive Jesus Christ? Colossians 2:6

_____

_____

4. What did Jesus say to those who would not obey him? Luke 6:46

_____

_____

5. According to Jesus, who will enter the Kingdom of Heaven? Matthew 7:21-23

_____

Personal Application

What did you learn from this lesson and how will you apply it to your life?

_____

_____

_____

The Narrow Door

The Bible teaches that we are saved by grace, not by our works. We can not earn our way to heaven by good behavior. We must receive the gift of Christ's work on the cross. However, when true salvation occurs the evidence of our changed lives should be obvious.

Read Matthew 7:13-20.

1. Describe the entrance to the kingdom of God.

   v. 13, 14 _____

2. How can we tell who is "real" and who is not?

   v. 16 _____

3. What is the destiny of those who bear bad fruit?

   v. 19 _____

Bad fruit is another term for a sinful lifestyle. Sin is lawlessness. Sin is breaking God's commands.

4. What are God's commandments? Exodus 20:1-17

   v. 3 _____

   v. 4-6 _____

   v. 7 _____

   v. 8-10 _____

   v. 12 _____

   v. 13 _____

   v. 14 _____

   v. 15 _____

   v. 16 _____

   v. 17 _____

5. What did Jesus say about those who disregarded these laws?
Matthew 5:17-19

_____

_____

6. What leads us to Christ? Galatians 3:24

_____

_____

7. What does God promise to those who obey?   To those who disobey?
Deuteronomy 11:26-28

_____

_____

_____

8. What is the difference between those who love Jesus and those who do not? John 14:15,24

_____

_____

_____

The law shows us how sinful we are. It shows us the great need we have for a Savior. Christ's death on the cross has accomplished what no one could do on their own. Yet, we are not saved to continue living in sin.

9. What did Paul say must not be in our lives as believers?
Ephesians 5:3-5

_____

_____

_____

10. What did he warn would happen to those who practiced such things?
Galatians 5:19-21

_____

_____

_____

11. What is the reason people live in sin and still think they are Christians?
1 Corinthians 6:9-11

_____

_____

_____

Personal Application

What did you learn from this lesson and how will you apply it to your life?

_____

_____

_____

LESSON 3 **Lordship and Fellowship**

1. Who should we not have fellowship with? 1 Corinthians 5:11

_____

_____

2. What did Paul say the church should have done in this case of gross immorality? 1 Corinthians 5:1,2

_____

_____

3. What did Paul say about fellowship with unbelievers?
2 Corinthians 6:14-16

_____

_____

4. What does God command? 2 Corinthians 6:17

_____

5. What does God promise? 2 Corinthians 6:18

_____

6. Why is it important that we come out from close fellowship with unbelievers? 1 Corinthians 15:33

_____

7. What is friendship with the world? James 4:4

_____

8. If anyone chooses to be a friend of the world, what does he become?
James 4:4

_____

9. What are the benefits of Christian fellowship? Ecclesiastes 4:9-12

    v. 9 _____

    v.10 _____

    v. 11 _____

    v. 12 _____

Personal Application

What did you learn from this lesson and how will you apply it to your life?

_____

_____

_____

LESSON 4   Can You Pass the Test?

The book of 1 John gives a series of situations by which we can
evaluate the real condition of our lives. Deception is a very powerful force.
The devil is the master deceiver.   Many have fallen under
the influence of his deception. Many have prayed prayers, attended Bible
studies, or even joined a church, but their lives have not been truly changed
by Christ.

1. What is the message that John proclaimed? 1 John 1:5

_____

_____

2. What does John say about those who claim to have fellowship with God
and yet walk in darkness? 1 John 1:6

_____

_____

3. What does the Bible say about the person who claims to be a Christian but does not follow God's commands? 1 John 2:3,4

_____

4. Anyone who claims to love God but hates his/her fellow believer is walking in _____. 1 John 2:9

5. What does John say about those who love the world? 1 John 2:15

_____

_____

6. How can you know the difference between the children of God and the children of the devil? 1 John 3:7-10

_____

_____

7. If anyone says he loves God and yet hates his brother he is a _____. 1 John 4:20

This may seem hard to us, but if we embrace the truth, we will be changed. Christ's death on the cross paid the price for our sin. His resurrection broke the power of sin and death. In light of the power of the cross we must not accept a gospel that does not transform our lives. In the next lesson we will examine our necessary response to the message of the Lordship of Jesus.

Personal Application
What did you learn from this lesson and how will you apply it to your life?

_____

_____

_____

Repentance
&
Baptism

3

Repent and be baptized,
everyone of you.
Acts 2:38

What Shall We Do?

1. What was the "bottom line" of Peter's sermon? Acts 2:36

_____

2. What did the people say in response to Peter's preaching? Acts 2:37

_____

3. What did Peter say they should do? Acts 2:38

_____

_____

_____

4. What did Peter say they would receive if they would repent and be baptized? Acts 2:38

_____

5. Who did this promise apply to? Acts 2:39

_____

_____

6. What else did Peter say? Acts 2:40

_____

7. What happened to those who accepted the message? Acts 2:41

_____

_____

8. Once they were added to the local body of believers, what did they do? Acts 2:42,46

_____

_____

_____

Peter preached the message of the cross, that Jesus was both Lord and Christ. The people were "cut to the heart." They responded by asking "What shall we do?"   The answer to their question was four-fold:
1. Repent
2. Be baptized
3. Receive the gift of the Holy Spirit
4. Be added to the Church

In this chapter we will study repentance and water baptism. The Holy Spirit and the Church will be covered in separate chapters.

Personal Application

What did you learn from this lesson and how will you apply it to your life?

_____

_____

_____

LESSON 2   Turning from Sin - Turning to God

In studying repentance, we must also study faith. It is impossible to have true repentance without faith. Repentance involves "turning from" sin and faith involves "turning to" God. Therefore, biblical repentance is a turning away from sin and a turning to God.

1. What are six foundational teachings of Christianity?
Hebrews 6:1,2

_____   _____

_____   _____

_____   _____

2. What is the inscription on God's foundation? 2 Timothy 2:19

_____

_____

3. What message did Jesus preach? Luke 13:2-5

_____

_____

4. What message should be preached in all nations? Luke 24:47

_____

_____

5. What happens when we repent and turn to God? Acts 3:19

_____

_____

6. Who does God command to repent? Acts 17:30

_____

_____

7. What did Paul preach? Acts 26:20

_____

_____

8. What is the proof of repentance? Acts 26:20

_____

_____

9. What should we do about our sins? Proverbs 28:13

_____

_____

10. True repentance involves confession of sin, turning away from sin and turning to God. What else is involved? Exodus 22:3

_____

Restitution is defined as "the returning or restoring to someone what is his; the act of making amends." (Webster Dictionary)

11. Zacchaeus desired to repent and make restitution for his sins. How did he propose to make restitution? Luke 19:8

_____

_____

12. How did Jesus respond to Zacchaeus? Luke 19:9

_____

_____

13. What leads us toward repentance? Romans 2:4

_____

14. Part of repentance is being sorry for our sins. What are the two types of sorrow and what do they produce? 2 Corinthians 7:10

_____

_____

15. Besides repentance, what else does godly sorrow produce?
2 Corinthians 7:11

According to the scriptures, repentance involves conviction of sin, sorrow for sin, turning from sin and a willingness to make restitution. However, repentance is still not complete without faith.

Personal Application

What did you learn from this lesson and how will you apply it to your life?

LESSON 3 Repentance and Faith

1. What did Paul say we must turn to, when we turn from darkness?
Acts 26:18

True conversion is like a two-sided coin. One side is repentance, the other side is faith. We cannot turn from something without turning to something else. All of this is a gift of God (Ephesians 2:8). It is by grace we are saved. This means we do nothing to earn it. We are dead in sin and unable to change ourselves (Ephesians 2:1).

2. In order to receive eternal life, what must we do? John 3:16

3. What did Jesus say we must do? Mark 1:15

4. How are we justified? Romans 5:1

_____

_____

5. What happens when we receive Jesus as Lord and Savior?
John 1:12-13

_____

_____

6. How does Jesus describe the new life we receive as a Christian?
John 3:3

_____

_____

7. What must we believe? 1 John 5:1,5

_____

8. What must happen if we are to come to Christ? John 6:44

_____

_____

Personal Application
What did you learn from this lesson and how will you apply it to your life?

_____

_____

_____

LESSON 4 Water Baptism

1. What happened to those who accepted Peter's message?   Acts 2:41

_____

_____

2. What did the men and women who believed Philip's message do?
Acts 8:12

_____

_____

3. After hearing the good news about Jesus, what did the Ethiopian eunuch desire to do? Acts 8:35,36

_____

_____

4. Jesus told his disciples to go and make disciples of all nations. What did he say to do with those disciples? Matthew 28:19,20

v. 19 _____

v. 20 _____

The New Testament presents the following four illustrations to help us understand water baptism.

> Burial and Resurrection (Romans 6:4,5)
> Crossing the Red Sea (1 Corinthians 10:1,2)
> Circumcision (Colossians 2:11,12)
> The Flood (1 Peter 3:20,21)

5. Paul compares Christian baptism to a burial. In order to be buried, a person must first die. What must we die to before we can be baptized? Romans 6:1-3

_____

_____

6. The Israelites passing through the Red Sea is a picture of baptism for us. Why were the Israelites fleeing from the Egyptians? Exodus 2:23; 3:7,9

_____

_____

7. What happened to the Egyptians? Exodus 14:22-28

_____

_____

_____

In the same way the Israelites were in slavery to the Egyptians, we were all slaves of sin. The Israelites were freed from their bondage by passing through the Red Sea. Baptism pictures the freedom from sin that Jesus purchased for us on the cross.

8. Paul says baptism is like a circumcision, not done by human hands, but a spiritual circumcision done by Christ. What is put off during this spiritual circumcision? Colossians 2:11,12

_____

_____

9. What did Peter say the flood water symbolized? 1 Peter 3:21

_____

_____

10. What is baptism a pledge of? 1 Peter 3:21

_____

_____

Peter teaches that it is not the "removal of dirt from the body" that saves us. In other words, it is neither the act of baptism, nor the water of baptism. "Rather it saves you by the resurrection of Jesus Christ." Once again we see the scriptures teach that we are saved by what he did (death and resurrection), and not by what we do (water baptism). Peter goes on to say that baptism is a pledge of a good conscience.

Each of these pictures show the old life being put away and new life emerging. In baptism, we publicly display what Christ did through his cross and resurrection. We also show that we have identified with this. We obey Christ's command to be baptized and thereby identify with the power of the cross and resurrection to deliver us completely from the power and authority of the life of sin.

And now what are you waiting for? Get up and be baptized and wash your sins away, calling on his name. Acts 22:16.

Personal Application
What did you learn from this lesson and how will you apply it to your life?

_____

_____

_____

The Holy Spirit
&
Spiritual Gifts

He will baptize you with the Holy Spirit and with fire.

Matthew 3:11

Who is the Holy Spirit?

After his heart-cutting sermon, Peter said the proper response would be to repent, be baptized and receive the gift of the Holy Spirit. It is impossible to live the Christian life apart from the power and presence of the Holy Spirit. He supplies the power we need to be a consistent witness for Christ.

1. Who is the Holy Spirit?

John 14:16 _____

John 14:17 _____

2. What are some ways the Holy Spirit helps the believer?

Matthew 10:19,20 _____

_____

John 14:26 _____

_____

John 16:13,14 _____

_____

Acts 1:8 _____

_____

Romans 8:14 _____

_____

Romans 8:16 _____

_____

Romans 8:26,27 _____

_____

2 Timothy 1:14 _____

_____

Personal Application
What did you learn from this lesson and how will you apply it to your life?

_____

_____

_____

LESSON 2 The Fruit of the Spirit

Read John 15:1-8.

1. How can we bring glory to the Father?

   v. 8 _____

2. What happens to the branches that do not bear fruit?

   v. 2 _____

3. What happens to the branches that do bear fruit?

   v. 2 _____

4. Why does he prune fruitful branches?

   v. 2 _____

5. Can we bear fruit by ourselves?

   v. 4 _____

6. What must we do in order to bear spiritual fruit?

   v. 4,5 _____

7. What does it mean to "remain in the vine"?

   v. 4-7 _____

8. List the fruit of the Spirit.   Galatians 5:22,23

   _____   _____

   _____   _____

   _____   _____

   _____   _____

   _____

9. Which is the greatest? 1 Corinthians 13:13

_____

10. Where is the Holy Spirit? 1 Corinthians 3:16

_____

Personal Application

What did you learn from this lesson and how will you apply it to your life?

_____

_____

_____

LESSON 3 # Spiritual Gifts

The fruit of the Spirit manifest God's character (love, joy, peace, patience, etc.) The gifts of the spirit manifest God's power. As his representatives on earth, we need to develop both.

1. List the "spiritual gifts" Paul mentions in Romans. Romans 12:6-8

_____   _____

_____   _____

_____   _____

_____

2. List the leadership gifts God has placed in the church.
Ephesians 4:8,11

_____   _____

_____   _____

_____

3. List the "manifestations of the Spirit" that are given for the common good. 1 Corinthians 12:4-11

_____   _____

_____   _____

_____   _____

_____   _____

_____

4. What attitude should we have regarding spiritual gifts?
1 Corinthians 14:1

_____

_____

5. What should be the motivating force behind spiritual gifts?
1 Corinthians 13:1,2

_____

_____

6. What does Paul say about the gift of prophecy? 1 Corinthians 14

v.3 _____

_____

v.4 _____

_____

v.31 _____

_____

v.39 _____

_____

7. What does Paul say about the gift of tongues? 1 Corinthians 14

v.2 _____

_____

v.4 _____

_____

v.14 _____

_____

v.15 _____

_____

8. What are we warned not to do?

1 Thessalonians 5:19, 20 _____

_____

_____

Ephesians 4:30 _____

_____

9. What did Jesus promise would happen to the disciples when the Holy Spirit came on them? Acts 1:8

_____

_____

Personal Application

What did you learn from this lesson and how will you apply it to your life?

_____

_____

_____

LESSON 4 The Baptism in the Holy Spirit

1. What did John the Baptist promise Jesus would do? Matthew 3:11

_____

_____

2. What did Jesus instruct his disciples to do after he ascended to heaven? Luke 24:49; Acts 1:4,5

_____

_____

3. Following are the five accounts of people receiving the Holy Spirit in the book of Acts. How did these people receive the Holy Spirit? What were the results or the manifestations of the Holy Spirit in each account?

Acts 2:1-6 _____

_____

_____

Acts 8:14-19 _____

_____

_____

Acts 9:17-19 _____

_____

_____

Acts 10:44-46 _____

_____

_____

Acts 19:1-6 _____

_____

_____

4. Who does the Father give the Holy Spirit to? Luke 11:13

_____

Personal Application

What did you learn from this lesson and how will you apply it to your life?

_____

_____

_____

Spiritual Hunger
&
God's Word

5

Man does not live on bread alone,
but on every word that comes
from the mouth of God.

Matthew 4:4

The Authority of the Word

1. What were the top two priorities of the Apostles? Acts 6:4

_____

_____

2. What were the early disciples devoted to? Acts 2:42

_____

_____

_____

3. What happened as the Word spread? Acts 6:7

_____

_____

4. What was the Word doing? Acts 19:20

_____

5. How were the scriptures originally given?

   2 Peter 1:20,21 _____

   _____

   2 Timothy 3:16_____

   _____

6. What does John say about the Word? John 1:1

_____

7. Who is the Word? John 1:14

_____

8. What do the following verses teach about the Word of God?
   Psalm 119:89 _____

   _____

   Psalm 119:160 _____

   _____

Isaiah 40:8 _____

_____

Isaiah 55:11 _____

_____

Matthew 24:35 _____

_____

John 17:17 _____

_____

9. What does the writer of Hebrews say about God's word?
Hebrews 4:12,13

_____

10. What will judge us on the last day? John 12:48

_____

Personal Application

What did you learn from this lesson and how will you apply it to your life?

_____

_____

_____

LESSON 2 The Benefits of the Word

1. What was God's command to Joshua and what was his promise if Joshua obeyed? Joshua 1:8

Command _____

_____

Promise _____

_____

2. Describe the man who meditates on God's word. Psalm 1:1-3

_____

_____

3. What are the scriptures useful for? 2 Timothy 3:16,17

_____   _____

_____   _____

4. How did Jesus overcome temptation and defeat the devil?
Matthew 4:1-11

_____

_____

5. How can a Christian walk in victory over sin?

Psalm 119:9 _____

_____

Psalm 119:11 _____

_____

6. List some of the ways the Word benefits the believer:

Proverbs 4:20-22 _____

Psalm 119:98 _____

Psalm 119:99 _____

Psalm 119:100 _____

Psalm 119:105 _____

Psalm 119:165 _____

Personal Application
What did you learn from this lesson and how will you apply it to your life?

_____

_____

_____

If a person is deprived of food and water for an extended period of time his physical body will weaken and eventually die. There is a spiritual parallel. The word of God is our spiritual food and water. As surely as we will die physically without food and water, we will die spiritually without the Word.

1. What was David's greatest desire? Psalm 27:4

_____

2. What was the condition of the sons of Korah's soul? Psalm 42:1,2

_____

3. What was the psalmist's attitude towards God's presence?
Psalm 84:1,2,10

_____

4. Who will be filled? Matthew 5:6

_____

5. What does it mean to "hunger and thirst for righteousness"?

_____

_____

6. What did David say about the Word and its importance in his life?
   Psalm 119:72 _____

   _____

   Psalm 119:103 _____

   _____

   Psalm 119:127 _____

   _____

   Psalm 119:113 _____

   _____

7. Describe Job's hunger for God's word. Job 23:12

_____

_____

_____

8. What did Jeremiah say about the Word? Jeremiah 15:16

_____

_____

Personal Application

What did you learn from this lesson and how will you apply it to your life?

_____

_____

_____

LESSON 4 Obedience

1. What happens if we only listen to the Word? James 1:22

_____

_____

2. Describe the man who only listens to the Word without putting it into practice. James 1:23-24

_____

_____

_____

3. What happens to those who hear and act on the Word? James 1:25

_____

_____

_____

4. How did the Bereans receive the preaching of Paul and Silas? How often did they read and study the Scriptures? Acts 17:11

_____

_____

_____

5. If we call Jesus our Lord, what should we do? Luke 6:46

_____

_____

_____

6. Describe what happens to the man who hears and puts into practice the Word. Luke 6:46-48

_____

_____

_____

7. Describe what happens to the man who only hears. Luke 6:49

_____

_____

_____

8. What do real disciples do? John 8:31

_____

_____

_____

9. What does the truth do? John 8:32

_____

_____

_____

10. What is the proof of our love for Jesus? John 14:21,23,24

_____

Personal Application
What did you learn from this lesson and how will you apply it to your life?

_____

_____

_____

Discipleship & Leadership

6

Follow my example,
as I follow the example of Christ.

1 Corinthians 11:1

The Command: Make Disciples

Jesus' command is to "go make disciples of all nations." This charge propelled the early followers of Christ into a strategic mission that involved not just preaching the gospel, but training the new believers as well. A disciple is a learner as well as a follower.

1. What did Jesus say we must do after baptizing a new believer? Matthew 28:20

_____

_____

2. As the word of God spread, what was the result? Acts 6:7

_____

_____

3. What command did Paul give to Timothy? 2 Timothy 2:2

_____

_____

4. Read 2 Timothy 2:3-6.

Paul compares the life of a disciple with the life of a soldier, an athlete and a farmer. He then tells Timothy that if he will reflect on these things, then the Lord will give him understanding. What can you learn from each of these illustrations about discipleship?

Soldier _____

_____

Athlete _____

_____

Farmer _____

_____

5. What are the scriptures useful for? 2 Timothy 3:16

_____

_____

6. How can we know we are truly a disciple? John 8:31

_____

7. How can a disciple become like his Master? Luke 6:40

_____

8. What are we not to be conformed to? Romans 12:1-2

_____

9. How are we transformed? Romans 12:1-2

_____

This means we are to replace our old thoughts with God's word.

10. How does Jesus compare the person who hears his word and acts upon it? Luke 6:48

_____

_____

11. How does he compare the person who hears and does not act upon his word? Luke 6:49

_____

_____

The Bible says he dug down deep, then laid a foundation on the rock. The most critical part of any house is the foundation. This is why, as a disciple, you must lay a strong foundation as well. These Bible studies are intended to do just that - to help lay the foundations listed in Hebrews 6:1-2 as well as other critical aspects of the Christian life. If you are discipling someone else it is important that you make certain that the person is well-grounded in these essentials.

12. What has Christ called us to? 2 Timothy 1:9

_____

13. Why did he call us? 2 Timothy 1:9

_____

14. What does the Bible say about those who are "in Christ"?
2 Corinthians 5:17

_____

We are called to a whole new life; we are not only forgiven of our sins, we are given new hearts. Because of this new heart we should yearn to follow Christ.

Personal Application

What did you learn from this lesson and how will you apply it to your life?

_____

_____

_____

LESSON 2 # The Cost: Absolute Surrender

1. What three things did Jesus say all his disciples must do? Mark 8:34

_____

_____

_____

2. How often should a disciple take up his cross? Luke 9:23

_____

3. Jesus compared discipleship to a war (Luke 14:31-33). What else did he compare it to? Luke 14:28

_____

_____

4. What should we do before we start building? Luke 14:28-33

_____

_____

5. What does it mean to "count the cost"?

_____

6. What has it cost you to follow Jesus?

_____

7. What happens if we are not able to finish? Luke 14:29,30

_____

_____

8. Who cannot be a disciple?

Luke 14:27 _____

_____

Luke 14:33 _____

_____

It is very critical to understand what is being said here, as well as what is not being said. Through God's grace he has called us to his kingdom. Being "born again" means that we have new life. Though salvation is a free gift, it costs us everything. Make no mistake: we cannot buy his love and forgiveness, yet it will cost us everything if we follow. If we want to be disciples, then we can have no other god before him.

Personal Application
What did you learn from this lesson and how will you apply it to your life?

_____

_____

_____

LESSON 3   Discipleship and the Cross

We must keep in mind the great difference between the cross of Christ and the cross that we pick up when we are disciples. Because of Christ's victory at the cross, we are freed from sin and made slaves of righteousness (Romans 6:17-18). We are given the power to pick up our cross and follow him through his triumph at his cross.

1. What happened at the cross? Colossians 2:15-17

_____

_____

2. Describe Paul's message to the Corinthians. 1 Corinthians 2:1-2

_____

_____

3. What is the message of the cross to the perishing? To the saved?
1 Corinthians 1:18

_____

_____

The cross is foolishness because it destroys self-effort. We marvel at the greatness of God's work in paying our debt of sin and delivering us from the power of evil.

4. What did Paul boast in? Galatians 6:14

_____

5. What happened in Paul's life through the cross? Galatians 6:14

_____

6. What do you think Paul meant when he said "I have been crucified with Christ"? Galatians 2:20

_____

_____

7. What did he mean by the phrase: "I no longer live, but Christ lives in me"? Galatians 2:20

_____

_____

Personal Application

What did you learn from this lesson and how will you apply it to your life?

_____

_____

_____

LESSON 4 Christian Character

Those who are disciples will bear the marks of the Lord in their lives. It is critical that we cultivate the fruit of a godly life as we follow Christ in discipleship.

Read 2 Peter 1:3-11.

1. What has God provided for us by his divine power? 2 Peter 1:3

_____

_____

2. How do we partake of his divine nature? 2 Peter 1:4

_____

3. What can we escape as a result? 2 Peter 1:4

_____

The most important mark of a disciple of Jesus Christ is godly character. We should never minimize the importance of the "gifts of the Holy Spirit," yet it is the "fruit of the Spirit" that identifies the true follower of Jesus. When instructing his disciples how to identify false prophets, Jesus said, *By their fruits you will recognize them* (Matthew 7:19-20). Many are gifted; yet, the real test is the character, habits and lifestyle of the individual. Though every disciple will be given gifts for the profit of the entire Body of Christ, it is the fruit of a godly life that we must cultivate if we are to bear the marks of a true follower of Jesus. Charisma is important. Character is essential.

4. What is the foundational "ingredient" to which everything else is added? 2 Peter 1:5

_____

5. List the necessary "additives" that Peter describes. 2 Peter 1:5-7

_____

_____

_____

_____

_____

_____

6. What will be the result of having these qualities in increasing measure? 2 Peter 1:8

_____

_____

_____

7. What is the condition of those without these character qualities? 2 Peter 1:9

_____

_____

8. What is the promise to those who develop this Christian character? 2 Peter 1:10

_____

9. Why should we rejoice in suffering?   Romans 5:3,4

_____

_____

_____

10. Why did James say we should consider trials as pure joy?
James 1:2,3

_____

_____

11. What results in our lives when perseverance finishes its work?
James 1:4

_____

_____

12. What is the connection between trials and maturity or character?
James 1:2-4

_____

_____

_____

Personal Application
What did you learn from this lesson and how will you apply it to your life?

_____

_____

_____

LESSON 5 Discipleship and Leadership

Jesus' original disciples became great leaders. Their lives and message impacted the world. They did not start out as leaders. They started as disciples. All leaders must first learn to follow before they can lead.

1. What did Jesus tell his first disciples to do? Matthew 4:19

_____

_____

2. What did Jesus promise his followers? Matthew 4:19

_____

_____

3. What was their response to his command and promise?
Matthew 4:20

_____

_____

After a season of intense personal discipleship, Jesus sent his followers
out on their own to practice what they had watched him do.

4. What did Jesus give his disciples authority to do? Matthew 10:1

_____

_____

5. What did they do with that authority? Mark 6:7,12,13

_____

_____

6. Did Jesus want his disciples to just follow him and watch him minister,
or did he want them to watch, learn and do all they saw him do?

_____

_____

Discipleship is about learning to follow Jesus. Jesus is no longer walking
on earth making disciples. He left that task to his followers. Therefore,
if we are to become disciples, we must be discipled by someone.

7. Who is discipling you?

_____

_____

Discipleship is the first step to leadership. We are not merely to be
followers and learners forever; we are to act on what we have learned
and we are to lead others as we have been led.

8. Who are you discipling?

_____

_____

Jesus discipled twelve men in a group setting for three years. This still seems to be the best pattern of discipleship - small groups.

9. Are you in a small group (cell group)? Who is the leader? When and where does the group meet?

_____

10. What did Jesus tell his discipleship group before he left earth? Matthew 28:18,19

_____

_____

_____

11. What are we to teach our disciples? Matthew 28:20

_____

_____

12. What is the difference in teaching someone facts and teaching someone to obey? Matthew 28:20

_____

_____

_____

_____

13. What was the final promise to all who attempt to make disciples? Matthew 28:20

_____

_____

_____

Personal Application
What did you learn from this lesson and how will you apply it to your life?

_____

_____

_____

Spiritual Family
&
Church Discipline

7

I will build my church, and the gates of Hades will not overcome it.

Matthew 16:18

The Victorious Church

Peter preached the inaugural sermon of the New Testament church. He told the people to repent, to be baptized and to receive the Holy Spirit. All who responded were then added to the local body of the believers — the church. Everyone who is saved, baptized and filled with the Holy Spirit today should also be added to a local church. Just as God sovereignly determines our parents and other family members, he also sovereignly chooses which spiritual family we are born into. The church is God's instrument for advancing his kingdom. He has no "plan B." The church is the only legitimate setting for walking out the Christian faith. No long-term "lone ranger" can be a true disciple of Christ. All who truly desire to follow Christ must find their place in a church family.

1. What did Jesus say about his victorious church? Matthew 16:18

_____

_____

2. Who is the Rock? 1 Corinthians 10:4

_____

3. Describe the ultimate destiny of the church. Ephesians 5:26,27

_____

_____

4. What were the first church members devoted to? Acts 2:42

_____   _____

_____   _____

5. Briefly describe early church life. Acts 2:43-47

    v. 43 _____

    v. 44 _____

    v. 45 _____

    v. 46 _____

    v. 47 _____

6. Comment on the generosity of the early church. Acts 4:32-37

_____

_____

Personal Application

What did you learn from this lesson and how will you apply it to your life?

_____

_____

_____

LESSON 2 ## The Body of Christ

1. What does Paul call the people of God? 1 Corinthians 12:27

_____

2. What does Paul say about the importance of each part of the Body of Christ? 1 Corinthians 12:14-20

_____

3. Who decides where each part of the body should function? 1 Corinthians 12:18

_____

4. What does Paul say to those who think they do not need the rest of the Body? 1 Corinthians 12:21

_____

5. What about the parts that seem to be weaker? 1 Corinthians 12:22-24

_____

6. How should the parts of the body treat each other? 1 Corinthians 12:25,26

_____

7. List the seven "ones" mentioned in Ephesians 4:4-6.

_____   _____

_____   _____

_____   _____

_____

8. What did Jesus ask for in prayer regarding the unity of his disciples? John 17:20-21

_____

9. What does the Bible call someone who stirs up dissension? Proverbs 16:28

_____

10. Proverbs lists seven things that are an abomination to the Lord. What is the seventh? Proverbs 6:16-19

_____

Personal Application

What did you learn from this lesson and how will you apply it to your life?

_____

_____

_____

LESSON 3 # Church Leadership

1. What offices of authority and leadership did God place in the church? Ephesians 4:11

_____   _____

_____   _____

_____

2. What is the purpose of this "five-fold" ministry? Ephesians 4:12,13

_____

3. How long will these gifts operate in the Church? Ephesians 4:13

_____

4. What is the result of being in a church where these five ministries are operating? Ephesians 4:14

_____

_____

5. How is the body of Christ joined and held together? Ephesians 4:16

_____

_____

Read Titus 1:5-9 and 1 Timothy 3:1-7.

6. Why was Titus left in Crete?

_____

7. Were the local church elders appointed or elected?

_____

8. Describe the qualifications for eldership.

_____

_____

9. What do these verses teach about an elder's marriage, children and home life?

_____

10. What was Peter's exhortation to the elders? 1 Peter 5:1-4

_____

_____

_____

Personal Application

What did you learn from this lesson and how will you apply it to your life?

_____

_____

_____

LESSON 4 Church Discipline

1. What are some of the responsibilities of pastors, elders and spiritual leaders?

Acts 20:28 _____

Acts 6:2,4 _____

John 21:15-17 _____

Ezekiel 33:1-9 _____

Ezekiel 34:2-5 _____

2. How should church members relate to their pastors, elders and spiritual leaders?

Hebrews 13:7 _____

Hebrews 13:17 _____

1 Thessalonians 5:12,13 _____

1 Thessalonians 5:25 _____

1 Timothy 5:17,18 _____

3. Who is the head of the church? Ephesians 4:15

_____

4. What is the foundation of the church? 1 Corinthians 3:10,11

_____

5. What should you do if you know your brother has something against you? Matthew 5:23,24

_____

6. What three steps should be taken to deal with sin in the church? Matthew 18:15-17

v.15 _____

v.16 _____

v.17 _____

7. What should happen to the church member who is consistently wicked and immoral? 1 Corinthians 5:9-13

_____

_____

Personal Application
What did you learn from this lesson and how will you apply it to your life?

_____

_____

_____

1. What were the early disciples devoted to? Acts 2:42

_____

Read 1 Corinthians 11:23-32.

2. What are we guilty of if we receive communion in an unworthy manner? 1 Corinthians 11:27

_____

_____

3. What should we do before we receive communion?
1 Corinthians 11:28

_____

4. What happens to us if we continue to receive communion and do not turn from sin? 1 Corinthians 11:29

_____

5. What can happen as a result of this? 1 Corinthians 11:30

_____

6. How can we avoid being judged? 1 Corinthians 11:31

_____

7. When God judges or disciplines his children, what is his motive?
1 Corinthians 11:32

_____

_____

8. If we have no discipline what are we? Hebrews 12:8

_____

_____

9. What will we share in as a result of this discipline? Hebrews 12:10

_____

10. What will this discipline ultimately produce? Hebrews 12:11

_____

Personal Application

What did you learn from this lesson and how will you apply it to your life?

_____

_____

_____

Prayer
&
Worship

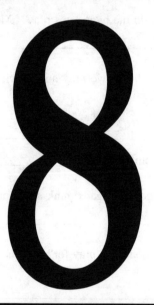

The prayer of a righteous man
is powerful and effective.
James 5:16

Personal Prayer

Christianity is more than just a religion. It is a relationship between God and man. All relationships grow through communication. The better the communication, the better the relationship will be. Communication is a two step process involving both talking and listening. God talks to us in many ways, but primarily through his Word. We talk to him through prayer. We listen to him as we read the Bible. He listens to us when we pray. We respond to his Word with action. He responds to our prayers with action.

By observing Jesus' personal prayer life, we find two keys to effective prayer: a specific time and a private place.

1. When and where did Jesus pray? Mark 1:35

   When _____

   Where _____

2. Where do the hypocrites pray? Matthew 6:5

   _____

3. Where should we pray and to whom should we pray?
Matthew 6:6,8,9

   Where _____

   To Whom _____

4. What do the pagans think about prayer? Matthew 6:7

   _____

5. What should we pray for? Matthew 6:9-13

   v. 10 _____

   _____

   v. 11 _____

   _____

   v. 12 _____

   _____

   v. 13 _____

   _____

Personal Application

What did you learn from this lesson and how will you apply it to your life?

_____

_____

_____

Do you have specific time set aside for daily prayer? When? Do you have a private place for prayer? Where?

_____

_____

LESSON 2 The Power of Prayer

1. What does Jesus promise to those who ask, seek and knock? Matthew 7:7,8

_____

2. What does Jesus say we must do in order to have our prayers answered? Mark 11:24

_____

3. What can we receive if we pray and believe? Matthew 21:22

_____

4. What does Jesus teach about prayer in the parable of the persistent widow? Why did he tell the parable? Luke 18:1-8

_____

_____

5. What can hinder our prayers?

Psalm 66:18,19 _____

James 1:6-8 _____

1 Peter 3:7 _____

6. In whose name should we pray? John 14:13-14

_____

7. Who should we present our requests to? Philippians 4:6

_____

8. How do we get to God? John 14:6

_____

9. How many mediators are there between God and man? Who is the only mediator between God and man? 1 Timothy 2:5

_____

10. What is the confidence we have in prayer? 1 John 5:14,15

_____

11. What were the results of the disciples' prayers? Acts 4:31

_____

12. What were Paul and Silas doing while in prison? Acts 16:25

_____

13. What were the results of their prayers? Acts 16:26-34

_____

14. What was Elijah's prayer request? James 5:17,18

_____

15. What was God's answer? James 5:17,18

_____

Personal Application
What did you learn from this lesson and how will you apply it to your life?

_____

_____

_____

LESSON 3 Corporate Prayer

1. What were the disciples doing as they waited for the day of Pentecost and the outpouring of the Holy Spirit? Acts 1:13,14

_____

2. What did the believers do when they heard of Peter and John's arrest and persecution at the hands of the Sanhedrin? Acts 4:23,24

_____

3. In the midst of persecution, what were their prayer requests?
Acts 4:29-30

_____

_____

4. What was the church doing while Peter was in prison? Acts 12:5,12

_____

5. How did God answer their prayers? Acts 12:7-12

_____

6. What were the Antioch church leaders doing when God called Saul
and Barnabas to the mission field? Acts 13:2

_____

7. What did they do before sending them off? Acts 13:3

_____

8. What is essential in corporate prayer? Matthew 18:19

_____

9. What did Jesus promise? Matthew 18:20

_____

Personal Application

What did you learn from this lesson and how will you apply it to your life?

_____

_____

_____

LESSON 4 Biblical Prayer List

1. What was Paul's prayer for the disciples in Ephesus?

Ephesians 1:17 _____

Ephesians 1:18 _____

Ephesians 3:16 _____

Ephesians 3:17-19 _____

2. What was Paul's prayer for the Philippian church?
Philippians 1:9-11

_____

_____

3. What was Paul's prayer for the Colossians?   Colossians 1:9

_____

_____

4. What did Paul instruct the Colossians to pray for? Colossians 4:2-4

_____

_____

5. What was Epaphras always doing for the Colossians?   Colossians 4:12

_____

_____

6. What was Paul's prayer request? 2 Thessalonians 3:1,2

_____

_____

7. What was Paul's prayer for Philemon? Philemon 4-6

_____

_____

Personal Application
What did you learn from this lesson and how will you apply it to your life?

_____

_____

LESSON 5 Worship

1. What kind of people is God seeking? John 4:23

_____

_____

2. How should we worship God? John 4:24

_____

_____

3. Our worship is to be in spirit and truth. What does God say about the use of physical idols, statues and images in worship?
Deuteronomy 5:8-10

_____

_____

4. What are we encouraged not to do? Hebrews 10:25

_____

_____

5. What internal attitudes make our worship acceptable to God?
Hebrews 12:28,29

_____

_____

6. What are some external expressions of acceptable worship?

Psalm 47:1,5,6 _____

Psalm 96:8,9 _____

Psalm 98:1,4-6 _____

Psalm 149:3 _____

Psalm 150:3-6 _____

7. In what two places did the early Church meet for worship and prayer?

Acts 20:20 _____

Acts 2:46 _____

Personal Application
What did you learn from this lesson and how will you apply it to your life?

_____

_____

_____

Faith
&
Hope

*Now faith is being sure
of what we hope for and certain
of what we do not see.*
Hebrews 11:1

What is Faith?

1. Faith is one of the few words that the Bible defines for us. What is faith? Hebrews 11:1

_____

2. What are some things you are certain of, but you do not see? (air, North Pole, God)

_____

3. How does faith come to us? Romans 10:17

_____

4. How does faith express itself? Galatians 5:6

_____

5. What do the following verses teach about faith?

Galatians 2:16 _____

Galatians 3:11 _____

Galatians 3:26 _____

Romans 14:23 _____

6. What is the foundation that must be laid in the life of every believer who wants to go on to maturity? Hebrews 6:1-2

_____

7. Who are we to put our faith in? Hebrews 6:1

_____

Personal Application

What did you learn from this lesson and how will you apply it to your life?

_____

_____

_____

False Faith vs. Real Faith

There are at least four types of "faith" that are really not faith at all: head faith, feeling faith, dead faith and crisis faith.

1. "Head faith" is merely agreeing to a set of religious creeds and historical facts about Jesus. What did James say about "head faith"? James 2:19

_____

2. The demons "believe" in God, but are they saved?

_____

3. Thomas is famous for having "feeling faith." His faith was based on his five physical senses. If his physical senses were convinced, then he would believe. What did Thomas say had to happen before he would believe? John 20:25

_____

4. Who did Jesus say would be blessed? John 20:29

_____

5. What should we do when our senses contradict our faith? 2 Corinthians 5:7

_____

6. What does James say about faith that is not accompanied by action? James 2:17

_____

7. "Dead faith" is a faith that does not translate into action. Can "dead faith" with no deeds save a person? James 2:14

_____

8. How should a true believer show his faith? James 2:18

_____

9. According to James, the body without the spirit is _____ and faith without works is _____. James 2:26

10. "Crisis faith" is also known as temporal faith. It is awakened by adverse circumstances. As soon as the bad circumstances change, crisis faith disappears without a trace. Why did the seed sown on rocky soil last only a short time? Matthew 13:20, 21

_____

11. The seeds that fell among the thorns were temporary. What were the "thorns" that choked the word? Matthew 13:22

_____

12. We have examined what the Bible says about four types of false faith. Real faith is not just in the head. It is not always confirmed by feelings. It must produce action and, it must last a lifetime. For faith to be real, where must it come from? Romans 10:10

_____

13. What does real faith believe? Romans 10:10

_____

Personal Application

What did you learn from this lesson and how will you apply it to your life?

_____

_____

_____

LESSON 3 Saving Faith

1. What must we do to be saved? Romans 10:9, 10

_____

_____

2. How are we justified? Romans 5:1

_____

3. What results from our justification? Romans 5:1

_____

4. How can we have access to God's grace? Romans 5:2

_____

5. Is man justified before God by obeying the law or by believing? Romans 3:28

_____

6. Who does God justify? Romans 3:26

_____

7. How does righteousness come? Romans 3:22

_____

8. How do the righteous live? Romans 1:17

_____

9. Paul spoke of a righteousness that did not come from the law. Where did it come from? Philippians 3:9

_____

10. How are we saved? Ephesians 2:8

_____

11. Who has the right to become a child of God? John 1:12

_____

12. Who will not perish but will have eternal life? John 3:16

_____

Personal Application

What did you learn from this lesson and how will you apply it to your life?

_____

_____

_____

LESSON 4 Faith and Obedience

1. God called Abraham to a place he had never seen. What did he do by faith? Hebrews 11:8

_____

2. What did Abel do by faith? Hebrews 11:4

_____

3. When God tested Abraham, what did he do by faith? Hebrews 11:17

_____

4. After he had grown up in the lap of luxury as the son of Pharaoh's daughter, what did Moses do by faith? Hebrews 11:24

_____

5. What did Moses choose by faith? Hebrews 11:25

_____

6. What else did Moses do by faith? Hebrews 11:27, 28

_____

7. What did all the Israelites do by faith? Hebrews 11:29

_____

8. What happened in Jericho after Joshua obeyed God's instructions? Hebrews 11:30

_____

9. Is it possible to be a man or woman of great faith and die without receiving the promise? Hebrews 11:37-39

_____

10. What does it mean to love God? 1 John 5:3

_____

11. Are God's commands a burden? 1 John 5:3

_____

12. How does John describe faith? 1 John 5:4

_____

13. Who overcomes the world? 1 John 5:5

_____

Personal Application
What did you learn from this lesson and how will you apply it to your life?

_____

_____

_____

LESSON 5 Mountain Moving Faith

1. The disciples failed to cast out a devil and asked Jesus "why couldn't we drive it out?" What was the reason they couldn't drive it out? Matthew 17:20

_____

2. Even if we have small faith in a big God, what can we do? Matthew 17:20

_____

There are two facts about God that serve as foundations for our faith. Abraham, the "father of our faith" understood these faith foundations. To be men and women of faith we must have unswerving faith in these two facts about God:

      1. God is powerful = God is able (Romans 4:21)
      2. God is faithful = God is willing (Hebrews 11:11)

3. What was Abraham fully persuaded of? Romans 4:21

_____

4. Some people ignore or deny the facts in a vain attempt to move in faith. What did Abraham do in regard to the physical facts? Romans 4:19

_____

5. What were the facts? Romans 4:19

_____

6. What did Abraham not do as he faced the facts? Romans 4:20

_____

7. Why was Abraham able to become a father? Hebrews 11:11

_____

8. What promise did God make to Abraham? Genesis 15:4-6

_____

9. What can the shield of faith do? Ephesians 6:16

_____

10. Who should we have faith in? Mark 11:22

_____

11. What must we do if we want our "mountain" to be "thrown into the sea"? Mark 11:23

_____

Personal Application

What did you learn from this lesson and how will you apply it to your life?

_____

_____

_____

Faith and Hope

1. What must we believe about God in order to come to him?
Hebrews 11:6

_____

2. What is impossible without faith? Hebrews 11:6

_____

3. What is the connection between faith and hope? Hebrews 11:1

_____

_____

4. What did the writer of Hebrews call hope? Hebrews 6:19

_____

5. What is the purpose of an anchor in a boat?

_____

_____

6. How does hope anchor our soul? What happens to a person who has
no hope?

_____

_____

7. Faith deals with today, hope with tomorrow. What are we now?
1 John 3:2

_____

8. What will happen to us when Jesus appears? 1 John 3:2

_____

9. How should this hope of seeing Jesus affect our lives? 1 John 3:3

_____

Personal Application

What did you learn from this lesson and how will you apply it to your life?

_____

_____

_____

Prosperity
&
Generosity

10

Give, and it will be given to you.
Luke 6:38

The Dangers of Wealth

1. What can choke out the Word and cause it to be unfruitful?
Mark 4:18,19

_____

_____

_____

2. What are some ways that people are deceived by wealth?

_____

3, What are some worries of life that choke the Word?
Matthew 6:25,28,31,34

_____

4. It is impossible to serve both God and _____. Luke 16:13

Jesus never made such a statement about anything else. He did not say, "you cannot serve God and power...God and sin...God and career...God and self." People know instinctively that they must serve God alone. But, because of the deceitful nature of money and wealth, many people think they are serving God, when they are actually slaves of money.

5. What can happen to those who want to get rich? 1 Timothy 6:9

_____

6. Do you want to get rich? What are some potential dangers of this desire?

_____

7. What is a root of all kinds of evil? 1 Timothy 6:10

_____

8. What happens to some people who are eager for money?
1 Timothy 6:10

_____

9. What happens to those who trust in money? Proverbs 11:4,28

_____

10. What should we guard ourselves against? Luke 12:15

_____

11. Read Luke 12:16-21. What is the point of the "Parable of the Rich Fool"?

_____

_____

Personal Application

What did you learn from this lesson and how will you apply it to your life?

_____

_____

_____

LESSON 2 Biblical Principles of Prosperity

Having established the dangerous nature of money, we can now look at what the Bible says about abundance and prosperity. Just because a thing is dangerous does not mean we should never use it. For example, cars are dangerous. Thousands are killed each year in automobile accidents. The proper response to this fact is not to walk everywhere, but to obey traffic rules. The proper response to the dangers of money is not to be poor, but to handle money according to God's law.

1. What were the Israelites told to remember about God?
Deuteronomy 8:18

_____

2. Read Deuteronomy 30:8-10. What is the relationship between prosperity and obedience?

_____

_____

3. What do the following scriptures teach about prosperity and God's provision?

Proverbs 10:3 _____

_____

Proverbs 10:4 _____

_____

Proverbs 10:22 _____

_____

Proverbs 13:21 _____

_____

Proverbs 13:22 _____

_____

Proverbs 21:21 _____

_____

Proverbs 22:4 _____

_____

Proverbs 22:9 _____

_____

4. What happens when we give?   What if we give with a small measure?
What if we give with a large measure?   Luke 6:38

_____

_____

5. How does the "Law of Sowing and Reaping" apply to money?
2 Corinthians 9:6

_____

_____

6. What kind of giver does God love? 2 Corinthians 9:7

_____

7. What is God able to do for the cheerful giver? 2 Corinthians 9:8

_____

8. Why does God make people rich? 2 Corinthians 9:11

_____

When talking about prosperity, the question is not, "Will God prosper
me?" The question is, "What will I do with God's abundant provision?"

Personal Application
What did you learn from this lesson and how will you apply it to your life?

_____

_____

_____

Putting God First

1. What did the Israelites do with the first portion of all God provided for them? 2 Chronicles 31:5,6

_____

2. What part should we give to God? Proverbs 3:9

_____

3. What happens as a result of giving the first part to God? Proverbs 3:10

_____

4. Should we give a tithe of everything, or only on our official salary? On the first part or the left-over part? Before or after taxes and other expenses? Leviticus 27:30-32

_____

5. Why were God's people under a curse? Malachi 3:9

_____

6. How do men rob God? Malachi 3:8

_____

7. How did God tell them to test him? Malachi 3:10

_____

_____

8. What did God promise to do if his people would give him the whole tithe? Malachi 3:10-12

_____

_____

Personal Application

What did you learn from this lesson and how will you apply it to your life?

_____

_____

_____

Are you a tither? Do you give God the first tenth of all income?

_____

Extreme Generosity

1. According to Jesus, who gave the most? Why? Luke 21:1-3

_____

2. Paul bragged about the generosity of the Macedonian believers. Describe their situation. 2 Corinthians 8:2

_____

_____

_____

Here is the Macedonian formula for generosity: severe trials plus extreme poverty plus overflowing joy equals rich generosity.

3. How much did the Macedonians give? 2 Corinthians 8:3

_____

_____

Some people spend all they can afford to spend. These people are always broke. Some people spend less than they are able to spend. These people are saving. Then, there is that special category of people who spend more than they have. This is called debt.

Applied to giving, this principle looks like this: Some people give less than they are able to give. These people are robbing God. Others give what they are able. This is called obedience. And still others sacrificially give beyond their ability. These extreme givers are called heroes of the faith.

4. Did Paul have to pressure them to give in the offering? What was their attitude towards giving? 2 Corinthians 8:4

_____

Personal Application
What did you learn from this lesson and how will you apply it to your life?

_____

_____

_____

What kind of giver are you?
- o   less than you can afford
- o   as much as you can afford
- o   more than you can afford

Evangelism
&
World Missions

11

*Go and make disciples
of all nations.*

Matthew 28:19

Everyone is a Minister

1. What ministry has God given to each believer? 2 Corinthians 5:18

_____

2. What message has God committed to us? 2 Corinthians 5:19

_____

3. What does reconciliation mean and why do people need to be reconciled to God?

_____

_____

4. What is an ambassador?

_____

_____

5. What does it mean to be "Christ's ambassador"? 2 Corinthians 5:20

_____

_____

_____

6. What was Paul's attitude towards sharing the gospel with non-Christians? Romans 1:14-16

v. 14 _____

_____

v. 15 _____

_____

v. 16 _____

_____

7. Who will be saved? Romans 10:13

_____

8. What must happen before they can call on the name of the Lord? Romans 10:14,15

_____

9. God sent Peter to preach the gospel to Cornelius' house. Who did Cornelius gather to hear Peter preach? Acts 10:24

_____

10. What happened to Cornelius' relatives and close friends? Acts 10:44-48

_____

_____

_____

_____

11. Where did Paul preach? Acts 20:20

_____

12. Who did Paul preach to? Acts 20:21

_____

13. What did Paul preach? Acts 20:21

_____

_____

Personal Application

What did you learn from this lesson and how will you apply it to your life?

_____

_____

_____

LESSON 2 Boldness

1. Under the threat of persecution, what did the disciples pray for? Acts 4:29

_____

2. What were the results of their prayer? Acts 4:31

_____

_____

_____

3. According to Baranabas, how did Saul (Paul) preach? Acts 9:27

_____

_____

4. Paul boldly preached to the Grecian Jews. What was their response? Acts 9:29

_____

5. After Saul's conversion, how long did he wait until he preached the gospel? Acts 9:19,20

_____

6. Describe the difference between a righteous man and a wicked man. Proverbs 28:1

Wicked man _____

Righteous man _____

7. What is the fear of man? Proverbs 29:25

_____

8. Paul requested prayers that he might preach the gospel in what manner? Ephesians 6:19,20

_____

Personal Application

What did you learn from this lesson and how will you apply it to your life?

_____

_____

_____

LESSON 3 Spiritual Warfare and Evangelism

1. What has happened to unbelievers? 2 Corinthians 4:4

_____

2. How are men taken captive? Colossians 2:8

_____

3. What did Jesus come to do? Luke 4:18-21

_____

_____

_____

4. Why did the Son of God appear? 1 John 3:8

_____

When we share the gospel with lost people, we are engaging in spiritual warfare. Jesus came to set the captives free. He frees people as we speak the truth.

5. Who are we struggling against? Ephesians 6:12

_____

_____

6. What happened when Paul preached? Acts 16:14

_____

7. What must happen if people are to come to Christ? John 6:44

_____

_____

Personal Application
What did you learn from this lesson and how will you apply it to your life?

_____

_____

_____

LESSON 4 Miracles, Signs and Wonders

1. When the disciples stepped out in faith and boldly preached the gospel, what happened? Mark 16:20

_____

_____

2. Why did the people in Samaria pay close attention to Philip?
Acts 8:6-8

_____

_____

_____

3. What were Paul and Barnabas doing when the lame man from Lystra
was healed? Acts 14:6-10

_____

Our part is to boldly preach and pray. As we do this, God will work
powerful miracles. We do the preaching; he does the healing.

4. What will happen if we lay hands on sick people? Mark 16:18

_____

5. What will the Father give us? John 15:16

_____

6. What did Jesus promise to those with faith? John 14:12

_____

_____

7. How can we see these greater works? John 14:13,14

_____

_____

8. How was the crippled man at the Beautiful Gate healed?
Acts 3:6,7,16

_____

_____

9. How much authority is in the name of Jesus? Matthew 28:18

_____

10. What happens at the mention of Jesus' name? Philippians 2:10,11

_____

11. What did Jesus say would happen if we have faith in him?
Mark 11:23,24

_____

12. What pleases God? Hebrews 11:6

_____

13. What did Jesus say about the power of faith? Mark 9:23

_____

_____

Personal Application
What did you learn from this lesson and how will you apply it to your life?

_____

_____

_____

LESSON 5 # To the Ends of the Earth

1. What did Jesus promise would happen when the Holy Spirit comes on us? Acts 1:8

_____

2. What is a witness?

_____

3. What does it mean to be Christ's witness?

_____

4. Where were they to be witnesses? Acts 1:8

_____

5. What was the first promise Jesus gave to his followers?
Matthew 4:19

_____

6. What was the last command Jesus gave his disciples? Matthew 28:19

_____

_____

7. What are we to do with the disciples we make? Matthew 28:19,20

_____

_____

8. What did Jesus promise to everyone who will "go and make disciples of all nations"? Matthew 28:20

_____

9. What is the condition of the world in relation to the gospel?

John 4:35,36 _____

_____

Matthew 9:35-37 _____

_____

10. What did Jesus say we should pray for? Matthew 9:38

_____

11. Jesus died on the cross to purchase people from where?
Revelation 5:9

_____

_____

Personal Application

What did you learn from this lesson and how will you apply it to your life?

_____

_____

_____

Resurrection
&
Judgment

12

...man is destined to die once,
and after that to face judgment.

Hebrews 9:27

Death and Resurrection

According to the Bible, all humans have three unavoidable appointments: death, resurrection and judgment. We will all die one day. We will all be judged. But, how will we appear before the judgment throne of God? As a disembodied spirit? No, because between death and judgment there will be a resurrection.

1. What is everyone appointed to do at least once? Hebrews 9:27

_____

2. Where will we all stand one day? Romans 14:10

_____

3. Did Paul fear death? Why not? Philippians 1:21

_____

_____

There are three basic views of death. Only one is based on God's Word.

Annihilationism teaches that human existence is completely terminated by physical death, thus denying the existence of the soul and the justice of God.

Reincarnation teaches that upon death the souls of men and animals pass into new bodies of the same or different species as punishment or reward, denying the biblical doctrine of eternal judgment.

Resurrection is the Christian teaching that the dead shall all rise and be judged with eternal damnation or eternal rewards.

4. What did Paul say to those who said there is no resurrection? 1 Corinthians 15:13

_____

5. What if Christ was not really resurrected? 1 Corinthians 15:14-19

    v. 14_____

    v. 15_____

    v. 16_____

    v. 17_____

    v. 18_____

    v. 19_____

6. What is the last enemy Christ will destroy? 1 Corinthians 15:26

_____

7. How did Paul describe the resurrection body?
1 Corinthians 15:42-44

    v. 42 _____

    v. 43 _____

    v. 44 _____

8. Paul did not relate to Jesus as if he was still on the cross. How did
Paul want to know Christ? Philippians 3:10

_____

_____

9. What did Paul hope to attain? Philippians 3:11

_____

10. Where is our citizenship? Philippians 3:20

_____

11. What will our Savior do to our bodies? Philippians 3:21

_____

12. What was Paul's hope? Acts 24:15

_____

13. How did Paul's belief in the resurrection affect his life? Acts 24:16

_____

_____

14. To be alive "in the body" is to be _____.
2 Corinthians 5:6

15. To be "away from the body" is to be _____.
2 Corinthians 5:8

16. Where must we all appear one day? 2 Corinthians 5:10

_____

17. Who holds the power of death? Hebrews 2:14

_____

18. Who destroyed him? How? Hebrews 2:14

_____

19. Is it possible to be set free from the fear of death? How?
Hebrews 2:15

_____

_____

Personal Application

What did you learn from this lesson and how will you apply it to your life?

_____

_____

_____

LESSON 2 # The Justice of God and the Wickedness of Man

Many who do not know God and suppose man is basically good, ask:
"how can a loving God send people to hell?" But, once we see how
utterly sinful man is and how perfectly holy God is, we will ask: "how
can a holy God allow sinful men into heaven?"

1. What is the foundation of God's throne? Psalm 89:14

_____

2. What if we claim to be a Christian, yet "walk in darkness"? 1 John 1:6

_____

3. What if we claim to be without sin? 1 John 1:8

_____

4. What if we deliberately keep on sinning? Hebrews 10:26,27

_____

_____

5. What does it mean to "insult the Spirit of grace" and to "trample the
Son of God"? Hebrews 10:28,29

_____

_____

6. Why is it a "dreadful thing" to fall into the hands of the living God? Hebrews 10:30,31

_____

_____

7. What are stubborn and unrepentant people doing? Romans 2:5

_____

8. What can those who reject truth expect from God? Romans 2:6-8

_____

_____

9. What do those who believe in Jesus have? What about those who reject Jesus? John 3:36

_____

_____

10. How are we to speak and act? James 2:12

_____

11. What if we live a "pretty good life" and "do our best" to follow God, but disobey just once? James 2:10

_____

12. What is the moral condition of every human? Romans 3:23

_____

13. How can man be justified before God? Romans 3:24

_____

14. What did the sacrificial death of Christ demonstrate? Romans 3:25

_____

15. God is not only just, but also the one who _____.
Romans 3:26

Personal Application
What did you learn from this lesson and how will you apply it to your life?

_____

_____

_____

LESSON 3   The Judgment of Sinners

1. What comes after death? Hebrews 9:27

_____

2. Who will enter the kingdom of heaven? Matthew 7:21

_____

3. What will Jesus say to those who called him Lord, but did not really live under his lordship? Matthew 7:22,23

_____

_____

4. On judgment day, Jesus will "separate the sheep from the goats" or the righteous from the wicked. What are the only two eternal destinations after judgment? Matthew 25:46

_____

5. How is hell described in the following passages?

Matthew 13:41 _____

Matthew 25:41 _____

Mark 9:43 _____

Luke 16:23,24 _____

2 Thessalonians 1:9 _____

6. Who will be judged in hell?

Matthew 24:51 _____

Matthew 23:29-33 _____

Romans 2:8 _____

Revelation 20:15 _____

Revelation 21:8 _____

John 3:36 _____

7. What do the following verses teach about the "fear of God"?

Deuteronomy 10:12 _____

Ecclesiastes 12:13 _____

Isaiah 8:13 _____

Matthew 10:28 _____

Luke 1:50 _____

Acts 10:35 _____

Personal Application

What did you learn from this lesson and how will you apply it to your life?

_____

_____

_____

The Judgment of Saints

All who repent of their sins and put faith in Christ will be in heaven forever. Because God is just and our justifier, we will not be judged with those who die apart from Christ. But our life work will be judged, not to determine our eternal destination but to determine eternal rewards.

1. What does Jesus do? 1 Thessalonians 1:10

_____

2. What did Paul tell the believers in Rome? Romans 14:10,12

_____

_____

3. What did Paul tell the believers in Corinth? 2 Corinthians 5:10

_____

4. What will the fire test on judgment day? 1 Corinthians 3:13

_____

5. What will we receive if our work survives God's judgment?
1 Corinthians 3:14

_____

6. What if our lifework is burned up in judgment? 1 Corinthians 3:15

_____

7. What does James say about the judgment of spiritual leaders?
James 3:1

_____

8. What did David say about the death of a believer? Psalm 116:15

_____

9. Was David afraid of death? Why not? Psalm 23:4

_____

_____

10. What did John say about the death of a believer? Revelation 14:13

_____

11. What must we believe about God? Hebrews 11:6

_____

12. Athletes in ancient Rome competed for crowns made of perishable leaves and vines. What kind of crown does the Christian train for? 1 Corinthians 9:25

_____

13. What were Paul's thoughts about the possibility of making it to heaven (by the grace of God) only to be disqualified from receiving a crown? 1 Corinthians 9:26,27

_____

_____

14. What was Paul's crown? Philippians 4:1

_____

15. What was Paul's hope, his joy, his crown? 1 Thessalonians 2:19

_____

16. Who will be rewarded with the "crown of righteousness"? 2 Timothy 4:7,8

_____

_____

17. What reward does God give those who persevere under severe trials? James 1:12

_____

18. How faithful must we be to receive the "crown of life"? Revelation 2:10

_____

19. What reward will God give his shepherds who serve as overseers? 1 Peter 5:1-4

_____

20. What must we do to receive the "victor's crown"? 2 Timothy 2:5

_____

21. What spiritual activities does God promise to reward?

Matthew 6:3,4 _____

Matthew 6:6 _____

Matthew 6:16-18 _____

22. What do heavenly beings do with their crowns? Revelation 4:9,10

_____

_____

23. Why is God worthy of our crowns? Revelation 4:11

_____

Personal Application

What did you learn from this lesson and how will you apply it to your life?

_____

_____

_____

RESOURCES
FOR CHURCH-BASED
DISCIPLESHIP

Every Nation
PRODUCTIONS
www.everynationstore.com

NOTES

NOTES

NOTES

NOTES

NOTES

NOTES